Essential Audition Songs for Female Vocalists

£15.95

W34–1

pop ballads

International MUSIC Publications

International Music Publications Limited
Griffin House 161 Hammersmith Road London W6 8BS England

DON'T BE
A MUSIC
COPYCAT!

The copying of © copyright
material is a criminal offence
and may lead to prosecution.

Series Editor: Sadie Cook

Editorial, production and recording: Artemis Music Limited
Design & Production: Space DPS Limited

Published 1999

International MUSIC Publications

International Music Publications Limited
Griffin House 161 Hammersmith Road London W6 8BS England

International Music Publications Limited

England: Griffin House
161 Hammersmith Road
London W6 8BS

Germany: Marstallstr. 8
D-80539 München

Denmark: Danmusik
Vognmagergade 7
DK1120 Copenhagen K

Carisch

Italy: Via Campania 12
20098 San Giuliano Milanese
Milano

Spain: Magallanes 25
28015 Madrid

France: 20 Rue de la Ville-l'Eveque
75008 Paris

In the book

	page no	vocal range
Anything For You	6	
Do You Know Where You're Going To	12	
The Greatest Love Of All	22	
I Will Always Love You	17	
Killing Me Softly With His Song	34	
My Heart Will Go On	27	
Over The Rainbow	38	
Promise Me	43	
Walk On By	48	
The Way We Were	54	

On the CD...

Track 1   **Anything For You**

Track 2   **Do You Know Where You're Going To**

Track 3   **I Will Always Love You**

Track 4   **The Greatest Love Of All**

Track 5   **My Heart Will Go On**

Track 6   **Killing Me Softly With His Song**

Track 7   **Over The Rainbow**

Track 8   **Promise Me**

Track 9   **Walk On By**

Track 10   **The Way We Were**

Anything For You

Words and Music by
Gloria Estefan

Do You Know Where You're Going To

Words by Gerry Goffin
Music by Michael Masser

Moderato – with expression

Why must we wait so long___ be - fore we see

how sad the ans - wers to those ques - tions can be?___

CODA

know?

I Will Always Love You

Words and Music by
Dolly Parton

The Greatest Love Of All

Words by Linda Creed
Music by Michael Masser

24

My Heart Will Go On

Words by Will Jennings
Music by James Horner

Moderately fast

Ev' - ry night in my dreams I see you, I feel you,
that is how I know you go on.

way. You are safe in my heart and my heart will go on and on. on.

Mm

Killing Me Softly With His Song

Tempo rubato

Words by Norman Gimbel
Music by Charles Fox

Lyrics under staves:

Line 4–6:
I heard he sang___ a good song I___ heard he
I felt all flushed with fe - ver em - ba - rassed
He sang as if___ he knew me in___ all my

Line 7–9:
had a style,___ and so I came___ to see him and
by the crowd.___ I felt he found___ my let - ters and
dark des - pair,___ and then he looked right through me as

Over The Rainbow

Words by E Y Harburg
Music by Harold Arlen

42

Promise Me

Words and Music by
Beverley Craven

Walk On By

Words by Hal David
Music by Burt Bacharach

The Way We Were

Words by Alan Bergman and Marilyn Bergman
Music by Marvin Hamlisch